The Amazing

Dinosaur Sticker Book

Contents:

© 2019 Alligator Products Ltd
Published by Alligator Products Ltd
2nd Floor, 314 Regents Park Road, London N3 2JX
Retain this information for future reference.

Edited by Alexia Horner

Printed in China 0924

Dinosaurs

First in the Family

Over millions of years, early life forms have undergone many changes to create the animals and plants of the modern world. This process of change on our planet is called evolution.

There was life on our planet before the dinosaurs came into existence. The first animals lived in the sea. Then gradually, marine creatures called amphibians started walking on land. The first amphibians on land were the Acanthostega and Ichthyostega. Although they laid their eggs in water, they could live on land.

The Acanthostega was an early amphibian. It had fish-like gills, a long tail and fin. This creature had four legs that were not only used for walking on land but also for swimming.

The Hylonomus was one of the earliest reptiles. It was only 20 centimetres (8 inches) long and looked more like the modern-day lizard.

Reptiles evolved from amphibians. They were small creatures that could live on land, and could even lay their eggs on land. Amongst the first reptiles were the Cotylosaurs. Their skin was hard and full of scales. The eggs they laid had outer shells to protect them from the harsh, dry environment. The Hylonomous and Westlothiana belonged to this group.

The Erythrosuchus evolved from the Proterosuchus. But at 5 metres (16ft), it was much longer than its ancestor.

The dinosaurs evolved from a group of reptiles called Archosaurs. The word 'Archosaur' means 'ruling reptile'. Amongst the early Archosaurs were the Proterosuchus and Erythrosuchus. Both these reptiles were carnivores (meat-eaters) and ate other herbivorous (plant-eating) reptiles.

The Proterosuchus lived near rivers and streams. It was hardly 1.5 metres (5 ft) long and looked like the modern-day crocodile.

Over time the Archosaurs split into two groups. One led to the evolution of crocodiles, while the other led to the evolution of dinosaurs and birds.

Dinosaurs

The Dinosaur Age

Life on Earth has been divided into various historical periods called eras. There are six eras in total: Hadean, Archaean, Protezoic, Palaeozoic, Mesozoic and Cenozoic.

The dinosaurs appeared during the Mesozoic era. This era ran between 248 and 65 million years ago. It has been divided into three main periods of time: Triassic, Jurassic and Cretaceous. Dinosaurs appeared in the Triassic period and continued to evolve and rule the land for nearly 200 million years!

Although dinosaurs did not appear at the beginning of the Triassic period (248-206 million years ago), they had rapidly evolved towards the end of it.

One of the biggest differences between the first dinosaurs and reptiles was the way in which they walked. While reptiles had a sprawling lizard-like walk, the dinosaurs walked in a more upright way. The dinosaurs' limbs were held directly beneath their bodies, which allowed them to move more easily.

The Eoraptor is one of the oldest dinosaurs known to us. This meat-eater was also one of the smallest dinosaurs. It was one metre (3 ft) long and walked on its long hind legs.

The dinosaurs could be told apart by their hip-structure: Saurischians (lizard-hipped) and Ornithischians (bird-hipped). The Saurischians were then divided up by their feet: Theropods (beast-footed) and Sauropods (reptile-footed).

During the Jurassic period (206-144 million years ago) dinosaurs continued to change. The early Sauropods, like the Vulcanodon, grew much bigger evolving into giant dinosaurs like the Brachiosaurus and Seismosaurus.

The Vulcanodon was the ancestor of the Brachiosaurus. It was 6.5 metres (20 ft) long and lived on a diet of ferns and leaves. It had a long neck and tail, and walked on four huge legs.

The Anchisaurus lived during the Jurassic period. This plant-eater could walk on four as well as two legs.

It was during the Cretaceous period (144-65 million years ago), that the best-known carnivorous dinosaurs emerged. The famous Tyrannosaurus rex was amongst these, as well as the Ornithomimus and Deinonychus.

The Deinonychus was a fast and agile meat-eater. It is believed that these dinosaurs were extremely intelligent and hunted in packs.

5

Dinosaurs

Very Vegetarian!

Some of the biggest dinosaurs that ever lived were herbivores, which ate only plants. These gigantic creatures are called Sauropods and include the Diplodocus, Brachiosaurus, Maiasaura, Iguanodon, Stegosaurus and Triceratops.

BRACHIOSAURUS (JURASSIC PERIOD)

The Brachiosaurus is considered to have been the tallest of all the dinosaurs. It reached a height of around 12-16 metres (40-50 ft), and was about 26 metres (85 ft) long. Unlike other dinosaurs, its front legs were longer than its hind legs. It had an extremely long neck, which allowed it to feed on tall trees.

The Brachiosaurus is believed to have kicked its legs to defend itself from its enemies. But due to its size, this dinosaur did not have many enemies!

The name Maiasaura means 'good mother lizard'. The Maiasauras scooped out dirt to make holes in the ground and laid their eggs in them.

MAIASAURA (CRETACEOUS PERIOD)

The Maiasauras were duck-billed plant-eaters. It is believed that they lived in herds, which could contain vast numbers of these creatures. Over time, scientists discovered fossils of the Maiasauras together with fossils of their young and nests. This suggests that, unlike other dinosaurs, the Maiasaura looked after its offspring.

It is believed that the Iguanodon could walk on four legs and run on two. This plant-eater was over 9 metres (30 ft) long and 5 metres (16 ft) tall. It was the second dinosaur to be discovered.

IGUANODON (CRETACEOUS PERIOD)

The Iguanodon had a tough beak, which was filled with many teeth. Its tail was powerful and its hind legs were strong. On the end of the Iguanodon's thumbs were spikes, which could have been used for fighting, as well as for holding food. The rest of its fingers had hooves.

STEGOSAURUS (JURASSIC PERIOD)

The Stegosaurus is one of the most well-known dinosaurs. Its most distinctive feature were the large bony plates along its back. In the early days, scientists believed that these triangular plates were there to protect the dinosaur from its enemies. However, it was later discovered that the Stegosaurus used the spikes on its tail to fend off its enemies, which led scientists to believe that, in fact, the plates were there to regulate the dinosaur's body temperature.

The hind legs of the Stegosaurus were twice as long as its front legs. This has led scientists to believe that although this dinosaur walked on four legs, it probably raised itself on its hind legs to reach out for food.

Dinosaurs

Mad on Meat

Carnivorous dinosaurs are called Theropods. Most of them had long, strong legs that enabled them to run fast. Their big powerful jaws contained sharp teeth, and their front and hind legs had sharp claws. It is thought that some of these Theropods, like the Deinonychus and Velociraptor, hunted in groups.

TYRANNOSAURUS REX (CRETACEOUS PERIOD)

The Tyrannosaurus rex, often referred to as the T. rex, was one of the largest meat-eating dinosaurs. The T. rex had a huge head and a very powerful jaw, which contained many sharp teeth. The dinosaur's two strong legs enabled it to run very fast, but its huge frame stopped it from running very far. The stiff, pointed tail was used for balance and making swift turns when running.

The T. rex usually held its tail upright while running. This meat-eater could eat more than 200 kilograms (500 lbs) of meat in just one meal!

The Allosaurus was the biggest meat-eater of the late Jurassic period. Its name means 'different lizard'. The Allosaurus, with its S-shaped neck and unique backbone, was indeed different from other dinosaurs of that time.

ALLOSAURUS (JURASSIC PERIOD)

The Allosaurus roamed the Earth during the Jurassic period. It is believed that this dinosaur ate the large plant-eating dinosaurs, such as the Stegosaurus and Apatosaurus. Like other active Theropods, the Allosaurus walked on two legs. This dinosaur is considered to have been one of the most intelligent of its kind.

The Megalosaurus was the first dinosaur fossil to be discovered. It had a short but strong neck, and a large head with sharp teeth.

MEGALOSAURUS (JURASSIC PERIOD)

The Megalosaurus was the first dinosaur to be named. Its name means 'great lizard'. This powerful dinosaur was similar to other Theropods in appearance, reaching a height of 3 metres (10 ft).

VELOCIRAPTOR (CRETACEOUS PERIOD)

Not all dinosaurs were gigantic creatures. The Velociraptor was only 1 metre (3 ft) tall and 2 metres (6 ft) long. Yet, despite its smaller frame, this was one of the most deadly dinosaurs. The Velociraptor was so fast it could run up to 60 kilometres per hour (40 mph). It is thought that these dinosaurs hunted in groups, eating almost anything that came their way. It is also considered to have been one of the most intelligent dinosaurs.

The Velociraptor had a small head with 80 sharp, curved teeth and a flat snout. It had short arms in front with three clawed fingers and thin legs with four claws.

Dinosaurs

Dinosaurs with a Difference

Some dinosaurs had unique features that enabled them to defend themselves and, therefore, helped them to survive. For example, the Protoceratops, Pentaceratops and Triceratops all had horns, while the Stegoceras and Pachycephalosaurus were dome-headed, which meant they had very thick skulls.

In addition to the horns above its eyes, the Triceratops also had one short horn above its parrot-like beak.

TRICERATOPS (CRETACEOUS PERIOD)

A Triceratops looked very similar to a rhinoceros. This dinosaur had three horns on its head and a large bony frill on the back of its skull. It had one horn above each eye, approximately 1 metre (3 ft) long. Scientists believe that the Triceratops used its horns to attack its enemies by charging with its head lowered, much like the rhinoceros.

SPINOSAURUS (CRETACEOUS PERIOD)

This huge meat-eating dinosaur had a series of spines running down its back, which looked like a sail. The spines stretched as far as 2 metres (6 ft) high. It is thought that this `sail' helped to control the temperature of the dinosaur by attracting warmth from the sun, as well as cooling it down in the shade. Another dinosaur with a similar sail was the Ouranosaurus.

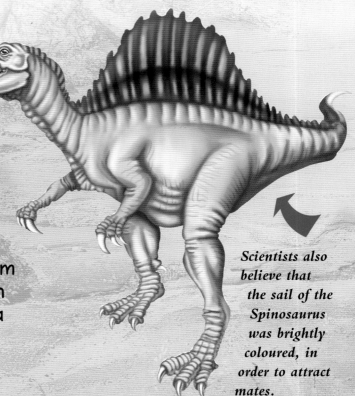

Scientists also believe that the sail of the Spinosaurus was brightly coloured, in order to attract mates.

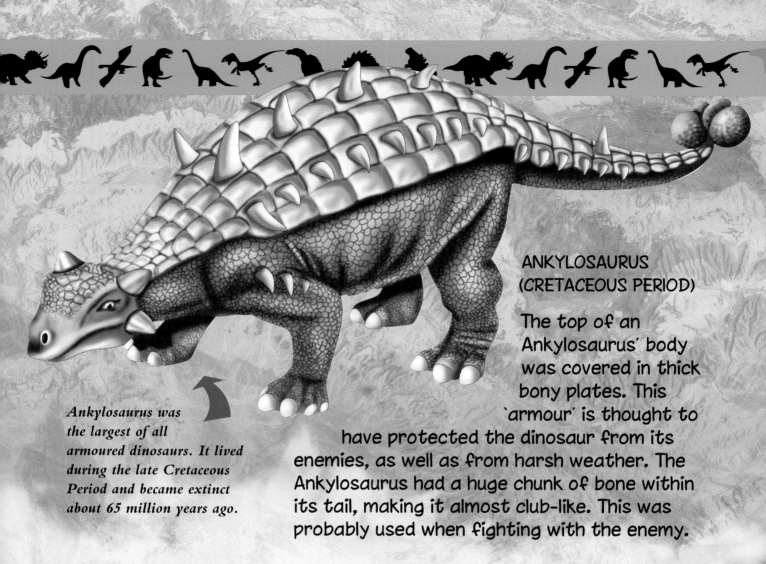

ANKYLOSAURUS (CRETACEOUS PERIOD)

The top of an Ankylosaurus' body was covered in thick bony plates. This `armour´ is thought to have protected the dinosaur from its enemies, as well as from harsh weather. The Ankylosaurus had a huge chunk of bone within its tail, making it almost club-like. This was probably used when fighting with the enemy.

Ankylosaurus was the largest of all armoured dinosaurs. It lived during the late Cretaceous Period and became extinct about 65 million years ago.

PACHYCEPHALOSAURUS (CRETACEOUS PERIOD)

This plant-eating dinosaur had a dome-shaped head, which was encircled with bumpy knobs. Scientists originally believed that this dinosaur used its thick-skulled head to ram its enemies during mating or power battles. However, more recent studies have proven that the skull of the Pachycephalosaurus was not so thick after all. Had the skull been hit hard, it would have broken and killed the dinosaur.

Although it is now clear that the Pachycephalosaurus did not engage in head-buttings some scientists still believe that these plant-eaters used their heads to ram into the sides of other animals. This way they wounded the opponent but avoided injury to themselves.

Dinosaurs

Reptiles of the Air and Sea

While dinosaurs roamed the land, flying reptiles ruled the skies and other reptiles lived in the sea. The flying reptiles were called Pterosaurs, which included the famous Pteranodon and Pterodactylus. Amongst the reptiles that lived in the sea was the Ichthyosaur, which had a fish-like appearance. Most of the other sea creatures did not look like fish.

The name Mixosaurus means 'mixed reptile'. This animal was given its name because it had features of both reptiles and fish.

MIXOSAURUS (TRIASSIC PERIOD)

The Mixosaurus had a long tail and fins. This reptile used its tail to swim through the water. Its long snout and sharp teeth enabled it to catch fish easily.

Other marine reptiles included the Ichthyosaurus, Nothosaurus, Plesiosaurus and Kronosaurus. The Nothosaurus had webbed feet, like a duck, which it used for swimming. It went ashore to lay its eggs. The Plesiosaurus had flippers, like a turtle.

GALLODACTYLUS (JURASSIC PERIOD)

The Gallodactylus was a medium-sized Pterosaur. Its wings measured around 1 metre (3 ft) in width. It was similar to another flying reptile called the Pterodactylus. The main difference was the crest on the back of the Gallodactylus' head. The Gallodactylus had a long beak with teeth that sat at the front of its jaw, helping it to catch fish.

The fossils of the Gallodactylus were first found in France, and was therefore called 'Gallic finger'!

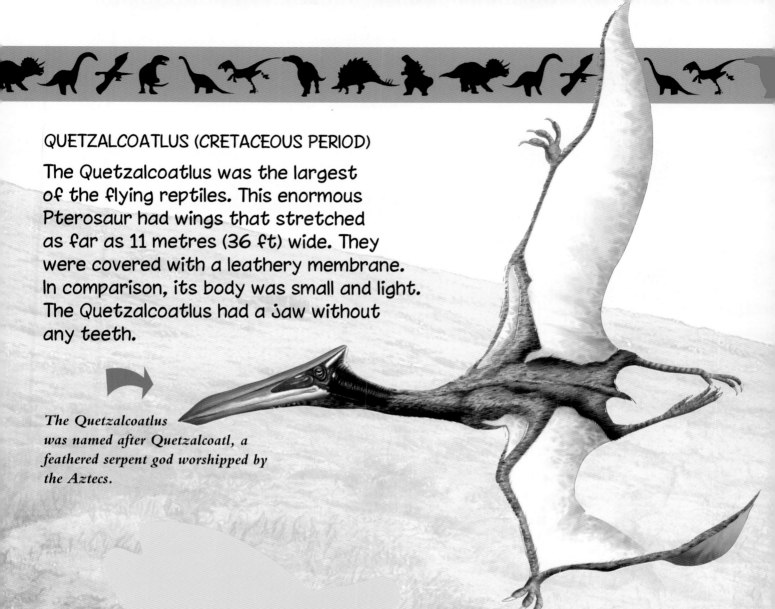

QUETZALCOATLUS (CRETACEOUS PERIOD)

The Quetzalcoatlus was the largest of the flying reptiles. This enormous Pterosaur had wings that stretched as far as 11 metres (36 ft) wide. They were covered with a leathery membrane. In comparison, its body was small and light. The Quetzalcoatlus had a jaw without any teeth.

The Quetzalcoatlus was named after Quetzalcoatl, a feathered serpent god worshipped by the Aztecs.

ARCHAEOPTERYX (JURASSIC PERIOD)

The Archaeopteryx is thought to have been the earliest bird in existence. Although it had wings these were not of the kind birds have today, as the Archaeopteryx had claws on its wings. It also had a long bony tail. The Archaeopteryx had many similarities to the dinosaur, including the shape of its skull and some of its bone structure. Despite having wings, it is believed that it may have had problems flying very far, for any length of time.

The first Archaeopteryx fossil was found embedded in a piece of smooth limestone that was used for printing. So the bird was named Archaeopteryx lithographica, meaning 'ancient wing from the printing stone'.

Dinosaurs

Identify the Dinosaur

Can you remember this rhyme...

Archaeopteryx swiftly took to flight

Acanthostega quickly swam out of sight

Brachiosaurus reached a dizzy height

Velociraptor went looking for a fight

Allosaurus went to take a big bite

Eoraptor looked up and got a fright

Sticker Fun Time

Find the correct stickers to fill the yellow spaces below. You may have already placed the stickers elsewhere in this book. See the rhyme opposite for clues!

Dinosaurs

Dinosaur Whiz Kid Quiz

1. Which one of the following is the tallest plant-eating dinosaur?

a) Tyrannosaurus rex
b) Brachiosaurus
c) Archaeopteryx

2. Which one of the following was the first amphibian?

a) Hylonomous
b) Acanthostega
c) Erythrosuchus

3. What does `Archosaur´ mean?

a) ruling dinosaur
b) ruling lizard
c) ruling reptile

4. Which dinosaur evolved from the Sauropods?

a) Coelophysis
b) Seismosaurus
c) Deinonychus

5. Saurischians were ....?

a) bird-hipped
b) mammal-hipped
c) lizard-hipped

6. Which dinosaur had bony plates along its back?

a) Maiasaura
b) Stegosaurus
c) Allosaurus

7. What does the name Megalosaurus mean?

a) bird-like
b) great lizard
c) big dinosaur

8. Which dinosaur was one of the largest meat-eating dinosaurs?

a) T. rex
b) Stegosaurus
c) Mixosaurus

9. Which dinosaur had three horns on its head?

a) Stegosaurus
b) Triceratops
c) Spinosaurus

10. Which was the largest flying reptile?

a) Archaeopteryx
b) Gallodactylus
c) Quetzalcoatlus

ANSWERS: 1. Brachiosaurus 2. Acanthostega 3. ruling reptile 4. Seismosaurus 5. lizard-hipped 6.Stegosaurus 7. great lizard 8. T. rex 9. Triceratop 10. Quetzalcoatlus